G000067386

The Hole Truth

Cartoons from *Sowetan, Mail & Guardian* and *Cape Argus*

FOREWORD BY ARCHBISHOP DESMOND TUTU

David Philip Publishers
Cape Town & Johannesburg

Acknowledgements: Thanks to my editors at the Mail & Guardian *(Philip van Niekerk, Anton Harber) and at* Sowetan *(Aggrey Klaaste, Mike Siluma, Mike Tissong, Sy Makaringe, Len Maseko) and at* Cape Argus *(Moegsien Williams, Shaun Johnson, Hugh Roberton) and the production teams for continuing to let me do my thing; Karina Turok and Tony Weaver for more brainstorming; my brother Alan for his thorough job of filing my visual references; all at David Philip; my parents and siblings for their continued support; and most of all my wife Karina.*

First published 1997 in southern Africa by
David Philip Publishers (Pty) Ltd,
208 Werdmuller Centre, Claremont 7700
in association with
Karina Turok & Jonathan Shapiro

ISBN 0-86486-352-7

Cover design by Jonathan Shapiro & Karina Turok
Reproduction by CMYK Pre-press

Printed by Clyson Printers (Pty) Ltd, 11th Avenue, Maitland, 7405, South Africa

Foreword by Archbishop Desmond Tutu

Thank you, Jonathan, for another wonderfully witty treasure. We are really fortunate to have you around to help us laugh at ourselves and at times cry inside when what you are depicting comes rather close to the bone of our unrealised dreams.

In South Africa we have had very fertile ground for the cartoonist's pen. The diversity of our nation and its young democracy gives endless opportunity for showing up our weaknesses and shortcomings, and Zapiro has impaled them on the sharpest of nibs. But if that were all Zapiro was about, his skill would be nothing more than a diversion. His genius lies in a natural gift combined with a passionate desire to will this country and its extraordinary people into realising their potential, to being good for each other and good for the world.
He wants us to grow up.

For my parents,
Gaby and Gershon

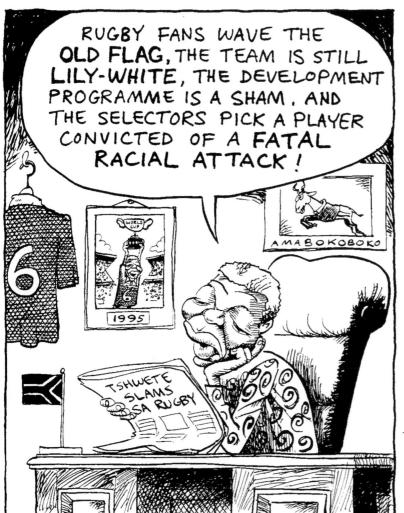

21 August 1996   Trevor Manuel is spotted shouting for New Zealand against South Africa

15 August 1996   Did the ANC government drop bribery charges against Sol Kerzner in return for favours? ANC maverick Holomisa thinks so.

THE HOLE TRUTH

23 August 1996

26 August 1996

2 September 1996   Finally expelled, Holomisa receives some support from a fellow-populist

3 September 1996

4 September 1996   At last it's official

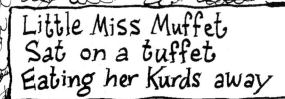
Little Miss Muffet
Sat on a tuffet
Eating her Kurds away

Along came a spider
And sat down beside her
And frightened Miss Muffet away.

6 September 1996

U.S. air strikes in Iraq

10 September 1996

11 September 1996

It's that AIDS play again

19 September 1996   The trial of Eugene de Kock. Convicted but not yet sentenced, the former head of the army's
Vlakplaas death farm starts talking.

20 September 1996

THE SA CATHOLIC BISHOPS CONFERENCE WANTS TO HAVE **ABORTION** DECLARED UNCONSTITUTIONAL...

Q. Until Catholic Bishops start experiencing

sex...   pregnancy...   childbirth...   parenthood..

... why should anyone listen to what they have to say on the subject ?

SOWETAN 23·9·96© ZAPIRO

23 September 1996

17

24 September 1996

25 September 1996   The composer Sontonga is honoured as the nation sings an awkward combination of anthems

27 September 1996

Israel's newly elected Prime Minister fulfils hardline expectations

21

WORLD-WIDE WEB

CRAIG WILLIAMSON

RUTH FIRST

JEANETTE SCHOON

OLAF PALME

DULCIE SEPTEMBER

apologies to olipliant

SOWETAN 2-10-96 © ZAPIRO

2 October 1996   Former apartheid agent linked to assassinations in many countries

3 October 1996

7 October 1996   Former Law and Order Minister Adriaan Vlok may be subpoenaed

8 October 1996

10 October 1996

Arrested in Angola

11 October 1996   . . . and named in Court

15 October 1996   Magnus Malan and other generals are acquitted of complicity in the KwaMakutha Massacre committed by SADF-trained IFP militia

18 October 1996

21 October 1996   Stix Morewa, President of the South African Football Association

23 October 1996

24 October 1996

29 October 1996

31 October 1996

13 November 1996

14 November 1996   Mandela says there will be no automatic succession to ANC leadership

18 November 1996

19 November 1996

The Presidential secretary who posed for Hustler Magazine

20 November 1996

21 November 1996   A visit to the Wilderness

22 November 1996

26 November 1996

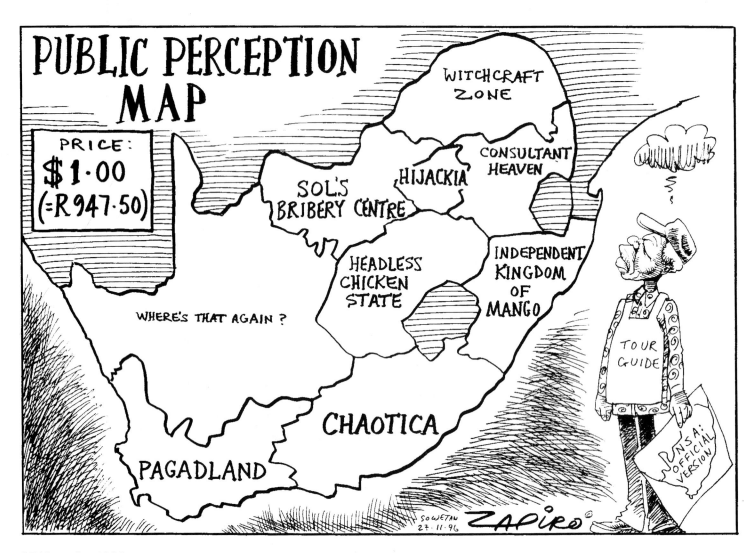

27 November 1996

28 November 1996

The ANC asserts central control

2 December 1996

3 December 1996

5 December 1996

6 December 1996

Mandela intervenes to assist Transport Minister Mac Maharaj

49

9 December 1996

Police Captain Brian Mitchell gets out of jail

16 December 1996

18 December 1996

20 December 1996

Brief appearance of "Boere Aanvals Troepe"

A new PAC President

SO KADER, WHAT'S THE STORY ON THE SYRIA ARMS SALE?

FIRING-CONTROL SYTEM FOR TANKS

WELL, ON THE ONE HAND, THE DEAL COULD EARN US BILLIONS!

...ON THE OTHER HAND, IT COULD MEAN AMERICA CUTTING OFF AID.

...ON THE OTHER HAND, THE U.S. HAS NO RIGHT TO **DICTATE** TO US!

...ON THE OTHER HAND, ISRAEL SAYS WE'RE UPSETTING THE BALANCE OF POWER IN THE MIDDLE-EAST.

...ON THE OTHER HAND, WHY SHOULD WE PANDER TO ISRAEL JUST BECAUSE THE WEST DOES?!

...ON THE OTHER HAND, SYRIA'S FOREIGN AFFAIRS AREN'T EXACTLY SQUEAKY-CLEAN...

...ON THE OTHER HAND, THE U.S. HAS A **CHEEK** TO BRAND SYRIA A TERRORIST STATE AFTER DECADES OF AMERICAN-SPONSORED RIGHT-WING TERROR!

...ON THE OTHER HAND, SYRIA **DOES** HAVE AN APPALLING HUMAN RIGHTS RECORD!

...ON THE OTHER HAND...

HANG ON, THAT'S ALREADY **EIGHT HANDS.**

DAMN ARMS TRADE— IT'S ALWAYS LIKE THIS!

16 January 1997

57

21 January 1997   Censured by the Pickard Commission for gross mismanagement, SAFA supremo Morewa hangs on

22 January 1997

23 January 1997

Professor Colin Bundy, eventually

27 January 1997

29 January 1997

The ruling party considers expanding the GNU

30 January 1997 — ANC national leadership replaces popular Free State Premier with Ivy Matsepe-Casaburri

3 February 1997

4 February 1997

6 February 1997   De Klerk tries to suppress access to previous Cabinet minutes, but revelations appear elsewhere

10 February 1997

11 February 1997

12 February 1997

Minister of Finance Trevor Manuel will soon announce his first Budget

"AN INSIDE JOB? ONE CAN'T RULE OUT THE POSSIBILITY..."

13 February 1997

14 February 1997

17 February 1997

18 February 1997

21 February 1997

20 February 1997   Racist remarks by Springbok coach André Markgraaff are secretly recorded

25 February 1997

26 February 1997

28 February 1997

3 March 1997

Resistance to Nkosi Johnson's admission

79

ANTI-GAY BILE

CANAAN BANANA'S HOMOSEXUALITY

SLIP!

ZAPIRO © SOWETAN 4-3-97

4 March 1997   Revelations about Zimbabwe's former President, the Reverend Canaan Banana

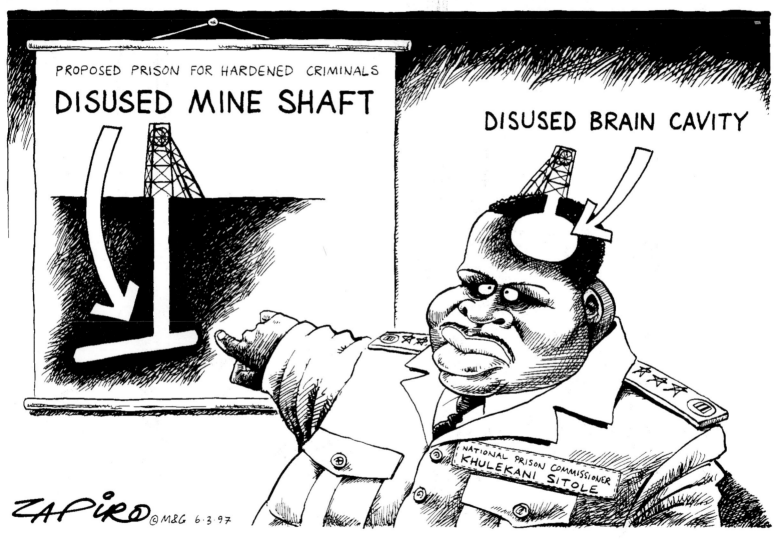

13 March 1997

14 March 1997   The apartheid regime's bio-chemical warfare doctor has re-surfaced in the current Defence Department

83

17 March 1997

19 March 1997   Israel begins a housing project for Jewish settlers on occupied Palestinian land

20 March 1997

24 March 1997

25 March 1997 Allan Boesak returns from America to face fraud charges. The Minister of Justice is at the airport to meet him.

26 March 1997

THE WORLD ACCORDING TO THE U.N. SECURITY COUNCIL AS PRESENTLY CONSTITUTED

3 April 1997

6 April 1997

An Eastern Cape faction doesn't recognise the new leader

7 April 1997

THE ORIGIN OF THE THIRD FORCE EXPLAINED

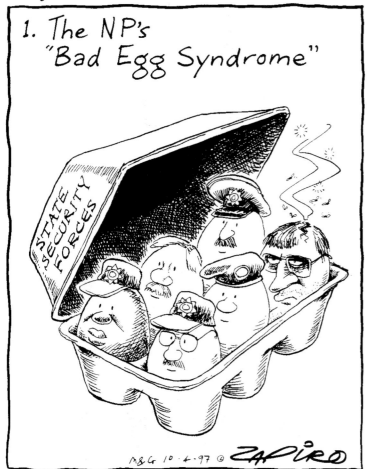

1. The NP's "Bad Egg Syndrome"

2. The Stench of Reality

10 April 1997

14 April 1997

15 April 1997

"WE THOUGHT YOU COULD USE SOME COMPETITION."

16 April 1997

17 April 1997

22 April 1997 Scrutiny of credit-card spending by the Interim Broadcasting Authority councillors

23 April 1997

24 April 1997

30 April 1997

6 May 1997

13 May 1997

14 May 1997   Fake licences available here

15 May 1997

16 May 1997   At the NP's second TRC appearance De Klerk denies knowledge of abuses

20 May 1997

Almost all IBA councillors resign in disgrace

22 May 1997 — Demoted reformist Roelf Meyer leaves the NP, aiming to restructure the political scene

26 May 1997

27 May 1997

CLARENCE MAKWETU IS FINALLY REMOVED FROM PARLIAMENT

28 May 1997   Expelled from the PAC for factionalism, the former PAC leader has refused to resign his seat

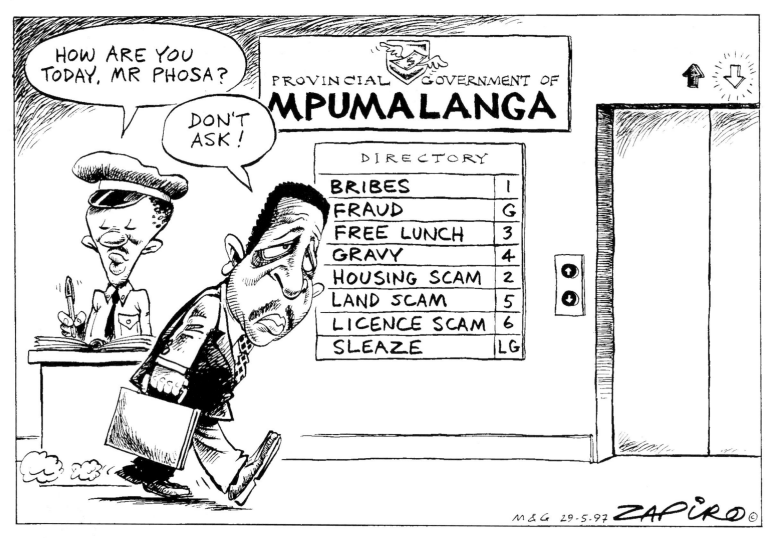

29 May 1997   Embattled Premier Mathews Phosa

2 June 1997

3 June 1997

5 June 1997

6 June 1997

9 June 1997   The Minister of Provincial Affairs is optimistic

11 June 1997   An alliance between Meyer's New Movement Process and Holomisa's National Consultative Forum

12 June 1997

16 June 1997

June 16 remembered

17 June 1997

19 June 1997   AWB leader sentenced to six years for assault of a petrol-pump attendant

123

23 June 1997

26 June 1997

30 June 1997

1 July 1997

3 July 1997

Hong Kong handed over

15 July 1997

17 July 1997

Warrant officer Jeff Benzien at the TRC

21 July 1997

29 July 1997

1 August 1997

President Daniel arap Moi

BILL OF RIGHTS

I. Every child has the right to be protected from maltreatment, neglect, abuse or degradation.

MAMOKGETHI MALEBANE

4 August 1997   A 7-year-old girl is raped and later murdered by the same man when he is released on bail

INTERNATIONAL RELATIONS TRANSLATED

5 August 1997

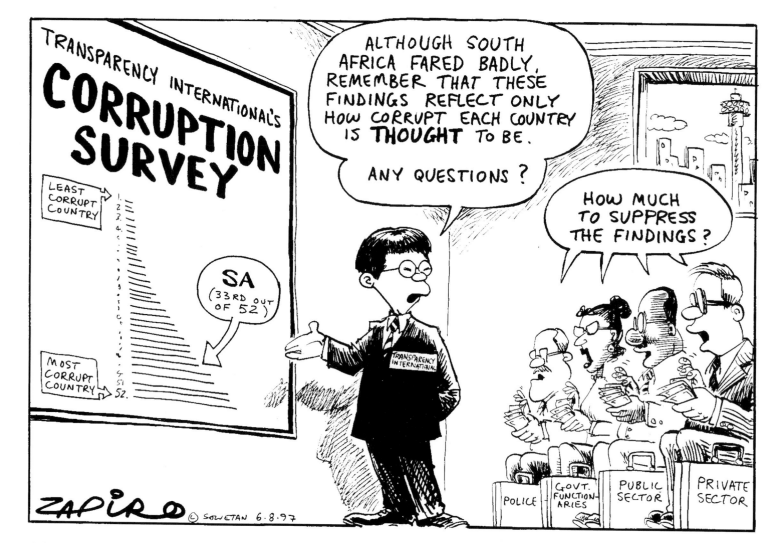

6 August 1997

7 August 1997

11 August 1997

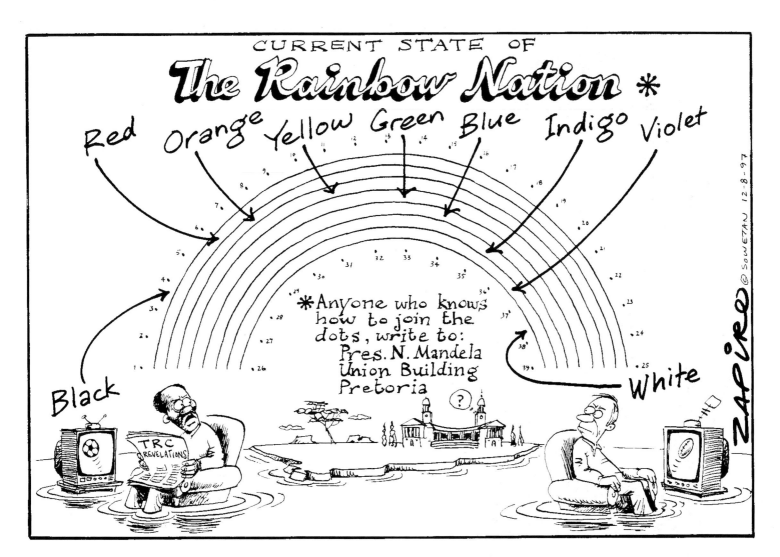

12 August 1997

The men who murdered Chris Hani

14 August 1997

CROSS-EXAMINATION

19 August 1997   George Bizos represents the Hani family at the Amnesty Hearing

143

18 August 1997

After the crucial victory over Congo

19 August 1997   IFP hardliner Walter Felgate defects to the ANC

20 August 1997

27 August 1997

1 September 1997

2 September 1997

OLYMPIAN GODS

Athens, Buenos Aires,
Cape Town, Rome or
Stockholm?

4 September 1997